Ed. 384

G. Schirmer's Editions
of
Oratorios and Cantatas

THE HOLY CITY

An Oratorio

For Full Chorus of Mixed Voices,
Soprano, Alto, Tenor, and Bass Soli,
with Piano Accompaniment

by

A. R. GAUL

(With Prologue)

G. SCHIRMER
New York / London

PREFACE.

THIS edition of the "Holy City" contains what I have for some time past felt was very necessary for its completion, viz., a Prologue. Indeed, this opinion has been so strong with me that I appeal to those who may after this time give performances of the work, always to include the new section, the words of which are of singular beauty and obviously appropriate.

As there are numerous instances, in choral works scored for an orchestra, of movements with organ accompaniment only (a plan which undoubtedly emphasizes the effect of the orchestra). I have, in the prologue, availed myself of this precedent, the orchestra being first employed in the movement "Contemplation."

In order to preserve the former paging of the work, Roman numerals are used for the Prologue.

ALFRED R. GAUL.

GILLOTT LODGE,

EDGBASTON, 1901.

THE HOLY CITY

THE treatment of the subject of this work is almost entirely reflective, the more dramatic parts of the book from which many of the numbers are taken, viz., the Vision of St. John, having already been treated in so masterly a manner by the great German composer, Louis Spohr, in his Oratorio, "The Last Judgment."

The first part of the "The Holy City" was suggested by the passages of scripture, "Here have we no continuing city," "Thy kingdom come," and sets forth the desire for a higher life, as expressed in the words, "My soul is athirst for God," which desire is followed by other passages expressive of the perfection of the higher life, such as "Eye hath not seen."

The second part was suggested by the words, "I saw a new heaven and a new earth, for the first heaven and the first earth were passed away," thus realising the desire and promises contained in the first part.

With the exception of two hymns, a verse from Milton, and three verses from the Te Deum, the words are entirely scriptural.

PROLOGUE.

QUARTET (UNACCOMPANIED).

Love not the world, nor the things that are in the world, for the world passeth away, and the lust thereof: but he that doeth the will of God abideth for ever.
Love not the world.

I. John ii. 15, 17.

SOLO.—*Soprano.*

For thus saith the Lord, he that overcometh shall inherit all things; and I will be his God, and he shall be My son.

Rev. xxi. 7.

CHORUS (ACCOMPANIED).

Love not the world.

QUARTET AND CHORUS.

Whoso is wise will ponder these things; and they shall understand the loving kindness of the Lord.   *Ps.* cvii. 43.

PART I.

CONTEMPLATION.

No. 1.—INTRODUCTION (INSTRUMENTAL).

No. 2.—CHORUS.

No shadows yonder?
　All light and song!
Each day I wonder,
　And say, "How long
Shall time me sunder
　From that dear throng?"

SOLO.—*Tenor.*

No weeping yonder!
　All fled away!
While here I wander
　Each weary day,
And sigh as I ponder
　My long, long stay.

QUARTET (UNACCOMPANIED).

No partings yonder!
　Time and space never
Again shall sunder.
　Hearts cannot sever:
Dearer and fonder,
　Hands clasp for ever.

CHORUS.

None wanting yonder!
　Bought by the Lamb,
All gathered under
　The ever-green palm;
Loud as night's thunder
　Ascends the glad psalm.

Bonar.

No. 3—AIR.—*Tenor.*

My soul is athirst for God, yea, even for the living God: when shall I come to appear before the presence of God?
My tears have been my meat day and night, while they daily say unto me, Where is now thy God?   *Ps.* xlii, 2, 3.
O bring Thou me out of my trouble..
　　　　　　　　　　　Ps. xxv. 17.

No. 4.—TRIO (UNACCOMPANIED).

Soprano, Mezzo-Soprano, and Contralto.

It shall come to pass that at eventide it shall be light.   *Zech.* xiv. 7.
And sorrow and sighing shall be no more.
　　　　　　　　　　　Isa. xxxv. 10.
For the former things have passed away.
　　　　　　　　　　　Rev. xxi. 4.

No. 5.—CHORUS.

They that sow in tears shall reap in joy: he that now goeth weeping shall come again rejoicing. *Ps.* cxxvi. 6, 7.

For God so loved the world that He gave His only begotten Son, that whosoever believeth in Him should not perish, but have everlasting life.

For God sent not His Son into the world to condemn the world: but that the world, through Him, might be saved.

St. John iii. 16, 17.

God is love. *I. John* iv. 8.

No. 6.—AIR.—*Contralto.*

Eye hath not seen, ear hath not heard, neither have entered into the heart of man the things which God hath prepared for them that love Him. *I. Cor.* ii. 9.

For He hath prepared for them a city, whose builder and maker is God.

Heb. xi. 10.

There remaineth, therefore, a rest for the people of God.

Therefore fear lest any come short of it.

Heb. iv. 9, 1.

No. 7.—CHORUS.

Treble and Alto Voices.

For thee, O dear, dear country,
 Mine eyes their vigils keep;
For very love, beholding
 Thy happy name, they weep.
The mention of thy glory
 Is unction to the breast,
And medicine in sickness,
 And love and life and rest.

Tenor and Bass Voices.

O one, O only mansion!
 O Paradise of joy!
Where tears are ever banished,
 And smiles have no alloy;
The Lamb is all thy splendour,
 The Crucified thy praise,
His laud and benediction
 Thy ransomed people raise.

Full Choir.

With jasper glow thy bulwarks,
 Thy streets with emeralds blaze,
The sardius and the topaz
 Unite in thee their rays;
Thine ageless walls are bonded
 With amethyst unpriced;
The saints build up its fabric,
 And the corner-stone is Christ.

Neale.

No. 8.—CHORUS.

Thine is the Kingdom, for ever and ever.

Matt. vi. 13.

I have looked for Thee, that I might behold
 and glory. *Ps.* lxiii. 3.

PART II.
ADORATION.

No. 9.—INTERMEZZO
(INSTRUMENTAL).

No. 10.—AIR.—*Bass.*

Thus saith the Lord, Behold, I create new heavens and a new earth; and the former shall not be remembered nor come into mind. But be ye glad and rejoice for ever in that which I create: for, behold, I create Jerusalem a rejoicing, and her people a joy.

Isa. lxv. 17, 18.

And I saw a new heaven and a new earth: for the first heaven and earth were passed away. And I saw the *Holy City,* New Jerusalem. *Rev.* xxi. 1, 2.

CHORUS (*at a distance from the Orchestra*).
Holy, holy, holy is the Lord of Hosts.

AIR.—*Bass.*

And I heard a great voice out of heaven saying, Behold the tabernacle of God is with men, and He will dwell with them, and they shall be His people, and God shall be with them, and be their God. And God shall wipe away all tears from their eyes; and there shall be no more death, neither sorrow, nor crying, nor any more pain; for the former things have passed away. *Rev.* xxi. 3, 4.

CHORUS (*at a distance from the Orchestra*).
Holy, holy, holy is the Lord of Hosts.

AIR.—*Bass.*

I saw also the Lord sitting upon a throne, high and lifted up, and His train filled the temple. Above it stood the Seraphim, and one cried unto another, and said, Holy, holy, holy is the Lord of Hosts.

Isa. vi. 1, 2, 3.

No. 11A.—CHORUS.—*For a Double Choir.*

Let the heavens rejoice, and let the earth be glad! let the sea make a noise, and all that therein is! *Ps.* xcvi. 11

No. 11B.—AIR.—*Tenor.*

To the Lord our God belong mercies and forgivenesses. *Dan.* ix. 9.

For like as a father pitieth his children, even so is the Lord merciful to them that fear Him. *Ps.* ciii. 13.

No. 12A.—AIR.—*Contralto.*

Then shall the King say, Come, ye blessed of My Father, inherit the kingdom prepared for you from the foundation of the world.
Matt. xxv. 34.

For it is your Father's good pleasure to give you the kingdom.　　　*Luke.* xii. 32.

No. 12 B.—SEMI-CHORUS
(UNACCOMPANIED).

The fining pot is for silver, and the furnace for gold : but the Lord tryeth the hearts.
Prov. xvii. 3.

No. 13.—AIR.—*Soprano.*

These are they which came out of great tribulation, and have washed their robes, and made them white in the blood of the Lamb; therefore are they before the throne of God, and serve Him day and night in His temple.
Rev. vii. 14, 15.

And they shall shine as the brightness of the firmament, and as the stars for ever and ever.　　　　　　　*Dan.* xii. 3.

No. 14.—DUET.—*Soprano and Contralto.*

They shall hunger no more, neither thirst any more; neither shall the sun light on them, nor any heat. And he that sitteth on the throne shall dwell among them. *Rev.* vii. 16, 15.

No. 15.—QUARTET AND CHORUS.
Treble and Contralto Voices.

List! the Cherubic host in thousand choirs
Touch their immortal harps of golden wires,
With those just spirits who wear victorious
　　palms
Singing everlastingly devout and holy psalms.
Milton.

SOLO.—*Bass.*

And I heard the voice of harpers harping with their harps; and they sung as it were a new song before the throne; and no man could learn that song but they which were redeemed.　　　　*Rev.* xiv, 2, 3.

No. 16.—CHORUS.

Great and marvellous are Thy works, Lord God Almighty; just and true are Thy ways, Thou King of Saints!　　　*Rev.* xv. 3.

To Thee all angels cry aloud, the Heavens and all the Powers therein. To Thee Cherubim and Seraphim continually do cry, Holy, holy, holy is the Lord of Hosts!
Te Deum.

Before the mountains were brought forth, or the earth and the world were made, Thou art from everlasting.　　　*Ps.* xc. 2.

Alleluia! Amen.

CONTENTS

The Holy City

Prologue
"Love not the World"

A. R. Gaul

10696r

ii

will, the will of God, a - bid - eth for ev - - - er. Love not the world, love not the world,

iii

love not the world, love not the world, nor the things, the_

love not the world, love_ not the world,

love not the world, love not, love not the world, the_

love not the world, love_ not the world,

things_that are in, are in the world. For

that are in, are in the world.

things_that are in, are in the world.

that are in, are in the world.

Solo Soprano

Allegro maestoso ♩= 144

Thus saith the Lord, He that o - ver - com - eth shall in -

her - it _ all things, and I will be his God, and he shall be My

son, he shall be My son,

he that o - ver - com - eth shall in - her - it all things,

and I _____ will be his God,

and he shall be My son,

I _____ will be his God and

he shall be _____ My son,

shall be My son, My son.

rit.

rit.

* During 4½ bars, play a continuous low B♭ on the *Pedals*.

Chorus

Tempo primo

vii

viii

ix

Part I.
Contemplation.
Nº 1. Introduction.

*) A Dotted Minim to be a little faster than a Minim in $\frac{2}{2}$ time.
The text of this work may be had separately.

X 10696

4

Nọ 2. "No shadows yonder."
Chorus, Tenor Solo and Quartet.

say, "How long Shall time me sun-der From that dear throng?"

say, "How long Shall time me sun-der From that dear throng?"

Tenor Solo.

No weep-ing yon - der! All fled a - way!

While here I wan - der Each wea - y day, _____

And sigh as I pon - der My long, long stay.

Quartet.

No partings yon - der! Time and space nev - er A - gain shall sun - der, _

No partings yon - der! Time and space nev - er A - gain shall sun - der, _

Unaccompanied

Hearts can-not sev - er: Dear - er and fond - er Hands clasp for ev - er. *rit.*

Hearts can-not sev - er: Dear - er and fond - er Hands clasp for ev - er. *rit.*

B Chorus.

None want-ing yon - der! Bought by the Lamb,

None want-ing yon - der! Bought by the Lamb,

All ga-ther'd un - der The ev-er-green palm —

All ga-ther'd un - der The ev-er-green palm —

ff *rall.* **C**
Loud as night's thun - der As-cends the glad psalm.

ff *rall.*
Loud as night's thun - der As-cends the glad psalm.

a tempo.
mf legato.

p *cresc.* *rall.* *dim.* *p*

Nº 3. "My soul is athirst for God."

(Air, Tenor.)

My soul is a-thirst for God, yea, e'en for the liv-ing God, When shall I come, come to appear be-fore the pres-ence of God? My tears have been my meat day and

out, out of my troub-le. O bring thou

me out of my troub-le, my troub - le,

My soul is a-thirst for God, yea, e'en for the liv-ing

God; When __ shall I come, come __ to ap-pear be-fore the

pres - ence, the pres - ence of God?

Nº 4. "At eventide it shall be light."

Trio (Unaccompanied.)

12

Chorus.

18

*) A Crotchet in this movement to be a little slower than a Dotted Crotchet in the previous move- ment.

20

10696

Nọ 6. "Eye hath not seen."
*Air (Contralto.)

*) An arrangement of this Air in the key of Bb (Original) will be found at the end of this work.

C Più mosso. (♩ = 88.)

par'd, pre - par'd for them that love Him.

For

He hath pre - par'd ___ for them ___ a cit - y, whose

build - er and Mak - er is God, He hath pre-

par'd, ___ pre - par'd ___ for them a cit - y, whose

build-er and Mak - er is God. Eye hath not seen,

hath __ not seen the things pre-par'd for them that love Him.

There re - main - eth, there-fore, a rest for the

peo - ple, the peo-ple of God; there-fore, fear, _____ there-fore,

fear, _____ lest an - y come short of it, there-fore,

№ 7. "For thee, O dear, dear country."

Chorus.

For thee, O dear, dear coun-try, Mine eyes their vigils keep; For ver-y love, be - hold-ing Thy hap-py name, they weep. The men-tion of thy glo-ry Is unc-tion to the breast, And med'-cine in

Mine eyes their vigils keep; For ver-y love, be - hold-ing Thy hap-py name, they weep. The men-tion of thy glo-ry Is unc-tion to the breast, And med'-cine in

sick - ness, And love, and life, and rest. O one, O on - ly man-sion! O Par - a - dise of joy! Where tears are ev - er ban - ish'd, And smiles have no al - loy; The Lamb is all thy splendor; The Cru - ci - fied thy praise, His laud and ben - e - dic - tion Thy ran - som'd peo - ple raise.

TENOR I. II.
BASS.

10696

SOPRANO.

With jas-per glow thy bul-warks, Thy streets with em'-ralds

ALTO.

TENOR.

With jas-per glow thy bul-warks, Thy streets with em'-ralds

BASS.

blaze; The sar-dius and the to-paz U-nite in thee their

blaze; The sar-dius and the to-paz U-nite in thee their

rays; Thine age-less walls are bond-ed With am-e-thyst un-

rays; Thine age-less walls are bond-ed With am-e-thyst un-

priced; The Saints build up its fab - ric, And the cor-ner-stone is

priced; The Saints build up its fab - ric, And the cor-ner-stone is

Christ.

Christ.

Christ.

Attacca Nº 8.

Nº 8. "Thine is the kingdom."

Chorus.

34

10696

36

Part II.

Nº 9. "Adoration."

Allegretto con moto. (♩ = 112.)

38

Nọ 10. A New Heaven and a New Earth.

Solo (Bass) and Choral Sanctus. *)

*) The Choral Sanctus to be sung at a distance from the Orchestra by a small Choir

glad and re-joice for___ ev - er in that which I cre - ate: for, be -

hold, I create, be - hold, I create Je - ru-sa-lem a re-joicing, and her

peo-ple a joy, Je - ru-sa-lem a re-joicing, and her peo - ple a joy.

And I

saw a new heav'n and a new earth, for the first heav'n and earth were pass'd a -

42

way,   were pass'd a - -way,   and I saw the Ho-ly_

Chorus.

SOPRANO. Slowly. *pp*

Ho - ly, Ho - ly, Ho - ly, Lord_of Hosts:

ALTO. *pp*

Ho - ly, Ho - ly, Ho - ly, Lord of Hosts:

TENOR. *pp*

Ho - ly, Ho - ly, Ho - ly, Lord of Hosts:

Cit - y, new Je - ru - sa - lem.   Tutti. *pp*

Slowly. ($\bullet$=40.)

Ho - ly, Ho - ly, Ho - ly, is the Lord of Hosts.

Ho - ly, Ho - ly, Ho - ly, Lord of Hosts.

Ho - ly, Ho - ly, Ho - ly, is the Lord of Hosts.

Tempo I.

10696

44

no_ more death, neither sorrow, nor cry-ing, nor an-y more pain, nor

Chorus.
G Slowly.

SOPRANO. *pp*
Ho - ly, Ho - ly,

ALTO. *pp*
Ho - ly, Ho - ly,

TENOR. *pp*
Ho - ly, Ho - ly,

Tutti.

an-y more pain, for the for - mer things have pass'd a - way.

G Slowly. (♩ = 40.)

Ho - ly, Lord of Hosts; Ho-ly, Ho - ly, Ho-ly is the Lord of Hosts.

Ho - ly, Lord of Hosts; Ho-ly, Ho - ly, Ho - ly, Lord of Hosts.

Ho - ly, Lord of Hosts; Ho-ly, Ho - ly, Ho - ly is the Lord of Hosts.

Solo.
I

Tempo I.

10696

saw al-so the Lord, sit-ting up-on a Throné,

high and lift-ed up, and His train fill-ed the Tem - ple.

A - bove it stood the Ser a - phim, and

one cried un - to an - oth - er and said:

Basses and Tenors of Chorus to sing in unison with Solo Bass.

Slowly. ($\quad$ = 40.)

Ho - ly, Ho - ly, Ho - ly, Lord of Hosts: Ho - ly, Ho - ly,

I Tempo I. ($\quad$ = 58.)

Ho - ly is the Lord of Hosts.

Harp.

Nº 11ª "Let the Heavens Rejoice."

Chorus for a Double Choir.

Allegro maestoso. (♩ = 120.)

Piano.

48

10696

50

10696

56

58

Nº 11ᵇ "To the Lord our God."

Air, (Tenor.)

Nº 12ª "Come, ye Blessed."
Air, (Contralto.)

Printed in the U. S. A.

66

10696

Nº12ᵇ "The fining pot is for silver."
Semi-Chorus. (*Unaccompanied.*)

Printed in the U. S. A.

gold; but the Lord, but the Lord tri - eth the

gold; but God the Lord tri - eth the

gold; but God the Lord tri - eth the

hearts, but the Lord, but the Lord tri - eth the hearts.

hearts, but God the Lord tri - eth the hearts.

hearts, but God the Lord tri - eth the hearts.

Nº 13. "These are they which came."
Air, (Soprano.)

Printed in the U. S. A.

came out of great trib - u - la - tion, these are they which

rit. *a tempo.*

came out of great trib - u - la - tion,

rit. *a tempo.*

and have wash'd, have wash'd their robes, and made them

a tempo.

white in the blood of the Lamb, these are

p

Ped.

they, these are they!

pp rit.

pp rit. *a tempo.*

R.H.

Ped. Ped.

Nº 14. "They shall hunger no more."
Duet.

76

78

№ 15. {"List! the cherubic host." *Quartet and Chorus.*+
{"I heard the voice of harpers." *Bass Solo.*

Moderato con grazia. (♩ = 120.)

+ Female voices only.

Printed in the U. S. A.

thou-sand choirs, Touch their im-mor-tal harps of golden wires, With those just spir-its that wear vic-to-rious palms, Sing-ing ev-er-last-ing-ly de-

vout,_____ de-vout and Ho - - ly psalms.

vout,_____ de-vout and Ho - ly psalms.

Chorus.

harp - ing with their harps, And they sang

as it were a new song, before the throne, be-fore the

throne, And no man could learn that song,

but

they, but they which were re - deemed,

cresc. *dim.* *rall.*

a tempo.

they which were ___ re - deemed. ___

u tempo.

Soprano Solo.

Bass Solo.

I heard the voice ___ of harp-ers,

p SOPRANO I.

List! the cher- u - bic host, list! the cher- u - bic host touch

p SOPRANO II.

List! the cher- u - bic host, list! the cher- u - bic host ___ touch

p CONTRALTO.

their harps, their harps of gold - en

harp - - ing with their harps, ___

their im-mor-tal harps of gold-en wires, ___

their im-mor-tal harps of gold-en wires, ___

Nº 16. Great and marvellous are Thy works.

Chorus.

Printed in the U.S.A.

90

works, mar-v'lous are Thy works, just and true are Thy ways, Thou King of

works, mar-v'lous are Thy works, just and true are Thy ways, Thou King of

are Thy

saints, mar-v'lous are Thy works, mar-v'lous are Thy works, just and

saints, mar-v'lous are Thy works, mar-v'lous are Thy works, just and

are Thy works, are Thy

true are Thy ways, Thou King_ of saints.

true are Thy ways,_ Thou King_ of saints.

B

10696

94

10696

Group 2

Solo Voices. *(Unaccompanied.)*

To Thee all An-gels cry a - loud, Mar - vel-lous are Thy

Mar - vel-lous are Thy

works, Lord God, The Heav'ns, and all the Pow'rs there - in. Mar-vel-lous

works, Lord God, Mar-vel-lous

are Thy works, Lord God, To Thee Cher-u - bim and Se - raph - im,

are Thy works, Lord God,

*)A Minim in ⅔ time to be of the same value as a dotted Minim in ¾ time.

Nº 6. "Eye hath not seen."

Air, (Mezzo-Soprano.)

Eye hath not seen, ear hath not heard, nei-ther have en-ter'd in-to the heart of man the things which God, which God hath pre-par'd for them that love Him, for them that love Him, the things which God hath pre-par'd, pre-

Printed in the U. S. A.